This Disney **MINNIE**
annual belongs to

....
Write your name here.

Age ....
Write your age here.

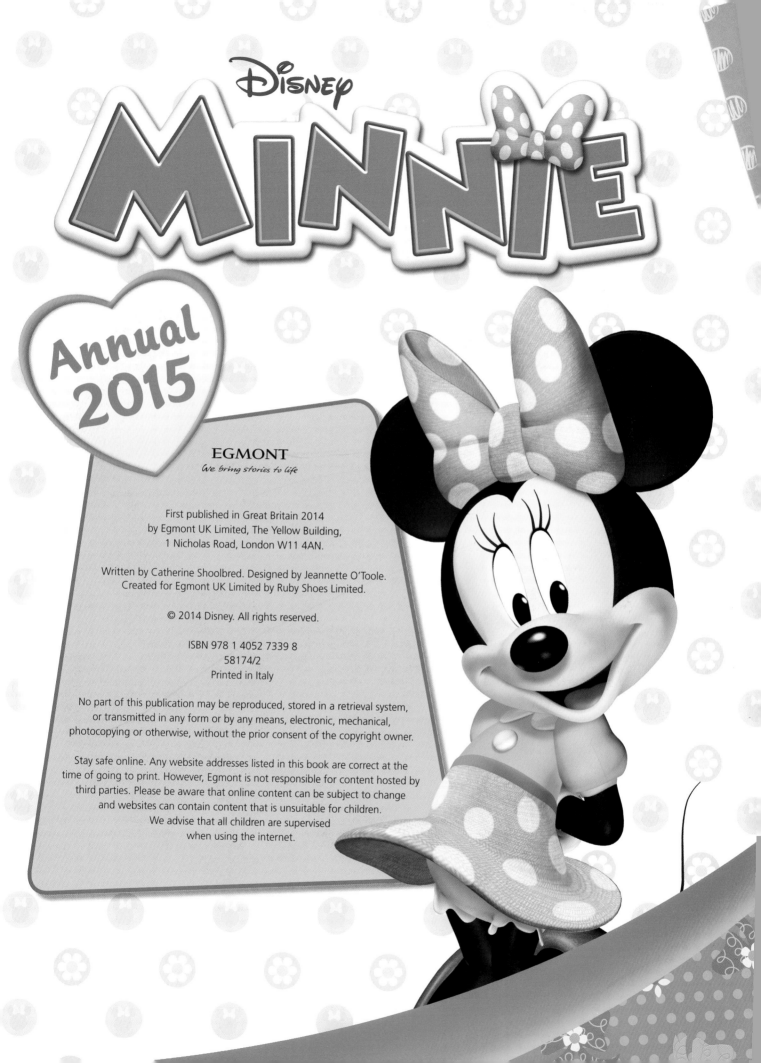

Disney Minnie

Annual 2015

EGMONT
We bring stories to life

First published in Great Britain 2014
by Egmont UK Limited, The Yellow Building,
1 Nicholas Road, London W11 4AN.

Written by Catherine Shoolbred. Designed by Jeannette O'Toole.
Created for Egmont UK Limited by Ruby Shoes Limited.

© 2014 Disney. All rights reserved.

ISBN 978 1 4052 7339 8
58174/2
Printed in Italy

Stay safe online. Any website addresses listed in this book are correct at the
time of going to print. However, Egmont is not responsible for content hosted by
third parties. Please be aware that online content can be subject to change
and websites can contain content that is unsuitable for children.
We advise that all children are supervised
when using the internet.

What's inside ...

Meet Minnie and Friends

Ta-da!

Minnie:
Busy Minnie owns the Bow-tique fashion shop and the cute Pet Salon!

Daisy:
Happy Daisy is Minnie's best friend. She makes outfits at the Bow-tique.

We did it!

Meow!

Cuckoo-Loca:
Little Cuckoo-Loca lives in a cuckoo clock in Minnie's Bow-tique.

Figaro:
Cute and cuddly Figaro loves playing with bows at Minnie's Bow-tique.

Aye-yi-yi

8

Millie and Melody:

Mischief-making Millie and Melody are Minnie's nieces. They love visiting the Bow-tique and Pet Salon.

Clarabelle and Bella:

Helpful Clarabelle fixes things in the Bow-tique. Her fluffy puppy, Bella, likes playing there too.

Oops! Sorry, Aunt Minnie!

Whoaaaa!

Woof!

Minnie and Daisy love spending time with **Mickey, Donald, Pluto** and **Goofy.** They always have lots of fun together!

Fashion Puzzles

Bow Sudoku

Help Minnie arrange the Bow-tique by colouring in the bows so there's one bow in each colour in each row across and down.

pink

blue

yellow

Answer on page 68.

Counting Clothes

Oh, no! Figaro's knocked over some shelves in Minnie's store! Count how many dresses, shoes and bags there are.

Add the numbers in the boxes.

dresses	bags	shoes

Answers are on page 68.

Minnie's Bow-tique Grand Opening

1

Minnie came to the clubhouse with news.
She told Mickey it was a special day.
Today she was opening her own BOW-TIQUE,
The grand opening was minutes away!

2

Mickey and Minnie went to the BOW-TIQUE.
All their friends cheered Minnie on.
A cut of the ribbon opened the store,
And then Minnie burst into song!

3

She sang, "Welcome to my new BOW-TIQUE,
Where each and every bow's unique!
If fun and fashion are what you seek,
Come inside and take a peek!"

4

Her friends looked around the BOW-TIQUE.
They found bows and bow ties that were fun.
Donald even found a neat camera bow tie.
There was something for everyone!

Pete watched while he hid nearby,
He wanted to get a new bow too.
But he'd never bought a bow before,
And he didn't know what to do.

Pete knocked over a rack of bows,
While sneaking around the shop.
He felt bad that he made a mess,
So he hid instead of cleaning it up.

"What a messy mess," Minnie sighed,
Looking at all her bows on the floor.
But her friends helped pick everything up,
And soon the shop was clean like before.

Pete was embarrassed he made such a mess,
All he wanted was a bow he could buy.
He opened a box to look for one,
And butterfly bows flew into the sky!

Get those bows, Pluto!

TRACE the path to help
Pluto catch the
flyaway bows.

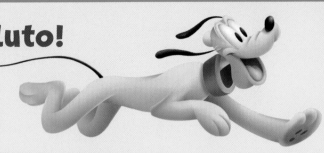

The fluttery bows flew everywhere,
Fluttering across the sky.
But Minnie needed to collect them all,
And they were flying up too high.

"How can we reach them?" Minnie asked.
And Goofy knew just what to do.
He took a swing with his great big net.
And caught all the bows as they flew.

The gang found where Pete was hiding,
He was sorry he had caused such trouble.
He wanted a bow for his Aunt Mabel,
But didn't want to cause any more muddle.

Minnie was happy to help Pete out.
She was sure she could find the right bow.
Since Mabel worked in a hot kitchen,
Minnie presented a cooling fan bow!

13

Pete said, "This is the perfect gift!"
Minnie had really made his day.
But when he turned the fan on as high as he could,
It blew all the other bows away!

14

The gang set out to get Minnie's bows.
Together they would fetch them all.
But the bows were at the top of trees,
And the trees they were in were tall.

15

Then someone came to help them out.
Coco the monkey who climbs trees.
She rushed up the trunks and got the bows
And she did it with real ease.

16

Thanks to Minnie's friends the bows were saved,
And it was time for the big bow show.
Everyone danced and sang together,
They were glad to have Minnie's great bows!

the end

Party Time

Use your favourite colours to make a party dress for Minnie. Don't forget to colour her bow too!

Minnie Mix Up

Minnie's new bows have got mixed up. Draw lines to join the pairs then circle the odd one out.

Answer on page 68.

Dotty Colouring

Join the dots then colour in Minnie.

Photo Close-Ups

Which of these close-ups appear in the big picture? Add ticks or crosses in the boxes.

1

2

3

4

Answers are on page 68.

Jet Set Puzzles

Fly Away Maze

Minnie's at the airport. Help her get to the plane and don't forget to pick up the things she needs along the way.

START →

FINISH

Answer on page 68.

Travel Words

Daisy and Minnie love travelling. Write over the dotted letters to complete these travel words.

TAXI

taxi

ticket

NAME Minnie

passport

plane

Can You Find?

Minnie and Daisy are on holiday. Help them find Figaro and Bella, 2 pink cases and 4 pairs of pink sunglasses.

Figaro Bella pink case pink sunglasses

Answers are on page 68.

Minnie on the Move

MINNIE ♥

Children can join in by saying the picture words as you enjoy Minnie's story.

 is very excited because she

is going on holiday today! First,

 needs to pack. She gets

her  and fills it with

 ,  and lots of

pretty  !

Use this key to help you read the story.

case **dresses** **taxi**

Minnie **shoes** **bows** **ticket** **Paris**

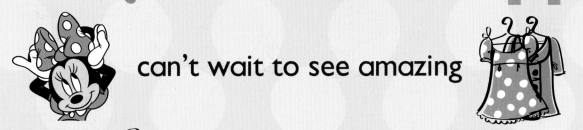

gets a [taxi] to the airport.

shows her [ticket] and boards

the [airplane]. Soon [Minnie] flies to [Paris]!

can't wait to see amazing [dresses]

and [shoes] in the French capital of fashion!

Write over the dotted word to show where Minnie is.

Paris

at Comes Next?

Help Daisy figure out what comes next in each row. Then draw it in the box.

Minnie Match Up

a

b

c

d

e

1 TAXI

2 NAME Minnie

3

4

5

Draw lines to match up the pairs. Then use pink to complete Minnie's picture.

Answers are on page 68.

Where's Daisy Going?

Follow the lines to see where Daisy is travelling to.

London

Paris

Answers are on page 68.

Spot the Difference

These pictures look the same, but there are 6 differences in picture 2. Can you spot them all?

1

2

Answers are on page 68.

Minnie

Picture Postcard

Hi Mickey,
Daisy and I are having a lovely holiday. We've eaten lots of ice cream! Wish you were here.
Love,

Minnie x

© Disney

Chef Minnie Matches

Minnie is a fantastic chef, and she knows exactly what she needs to cook everything just right! Do you?
MATCH each food to the right utensil. The first one has been done for you.

Answers are on page 68.

Minnie's Special Cookies

1

The dogs' home needed funds,
So Minnie had a new job to do.
"We'll make **COOKIES** for the bake sale,
And raise lots of money too!"

2

The friends put on their chef hats,
Minnie said, "Gather all we need!"
Daisy got milk and Goofy got eggs,
Everyone worked with speed.

3

"We're ready to start," Minnie cried,
"Everybody listen to me."
"Making **COOKIES** is very messy!"
Mickey said with glee!

4

The friends all worked together.
Daisy said, "This is so much fun!"
Soon they'd made lots of **COOKIES**,
Their job was almost done.

5

When the **COOKIES** were ready,
The friends gave them a try.
"They are yummy!" Goofy said,
"Good enough to buy!"

6

Seeing Pluto take a bite,
Gave Minnie a great idea.
"Let's make **COOKIES** for the dogs!
Give me a hand over here!"

7

It didn't take them very long,
Soon the dog **COOKIES** were done.
They were in the shape of bones,
There was something for everyone!

8

Later that day at the bake sale,
Mickey gave a loud shout,
"Let's give three cheers to Minnie,
Her dog **COOKIES** have sold out!"

the end

Meal Maze

Donald and Mickey have ordered a tasty dish to share at the restaurant. What is it? **FOLLOW** the path and ... **FIND OUT!**

START

Answer on page 68.

Odd One Out

Minnie's admiring her new bows. All have pairs in the picture except one. Can you spot the odd one out?

Write over the letters to reveal the odd bow's colour.

blue

Answer on page 68.

37

Millie and Melody

Colour Millie and Melody's bows then write over the dotted letters to complete the colour names.

green purple

Cuddle Time

© Disney

Summer Time

Daisy's Dress

Add colour to complete Daisy's new dress.

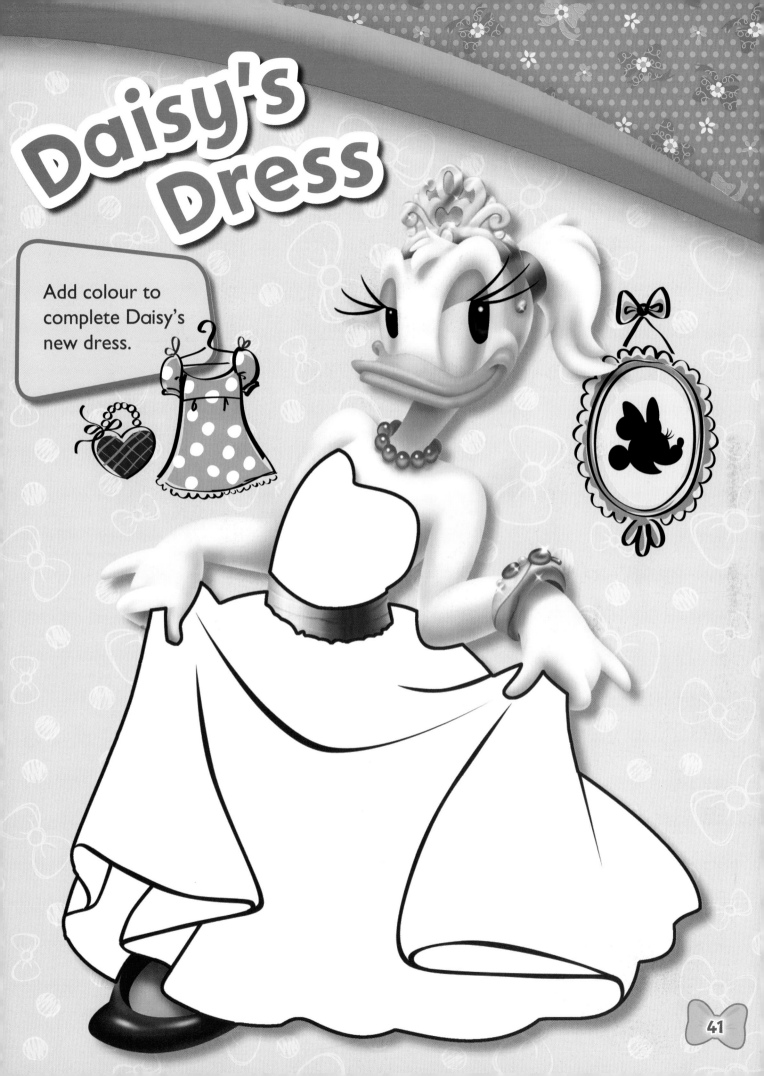

41

Shadow Friends

Match Minnie, Daisy, Figaro and Bella to their shadows.

42 Answers are on page 68.

Colours of the Rainbow

Mickey and his friends are ready for a new clubhouse adventure! Read the story, discover the wonders of the rainbow and learn new words and phrases.

Come and join the fun!

1 Minnie shows her friends a book about the **rainbow** ...

The **rainbow is an arch of light!**

2 Minnie tells her friends that the **rainbow** has many **colours**.

Look at these colours!

I can't count **them!**

3 There are **seven** of them as you can see here.

RED, **ORANGE**, **YELLOW**, **GREEN**, **BLUE**, **INDIGO** and **VIOLET!**

4 So Minnie has an idea; they will play a **rainbow game!**

Let's look for the **colours** of the **rainbow!**

Great idea!

5 In the garden, Mickey finds something **red** ...

LOOK! Strawberries are **red!**

Red is the first colour of the rainbow!

6 ... while Goofy drives his **orange** car.

Orange is the second colour of the rainbow!

7 Near the pond, Pluto finds some yellow ducklings.

Yellow is the third colour of the rainbow!

8 Minnie spots something **green** in a vegetable garden.

Cucumbers and peas are green!

9 Here's Donald, on his **blue** deckchair!

Blue is the rainbow's fifth band!

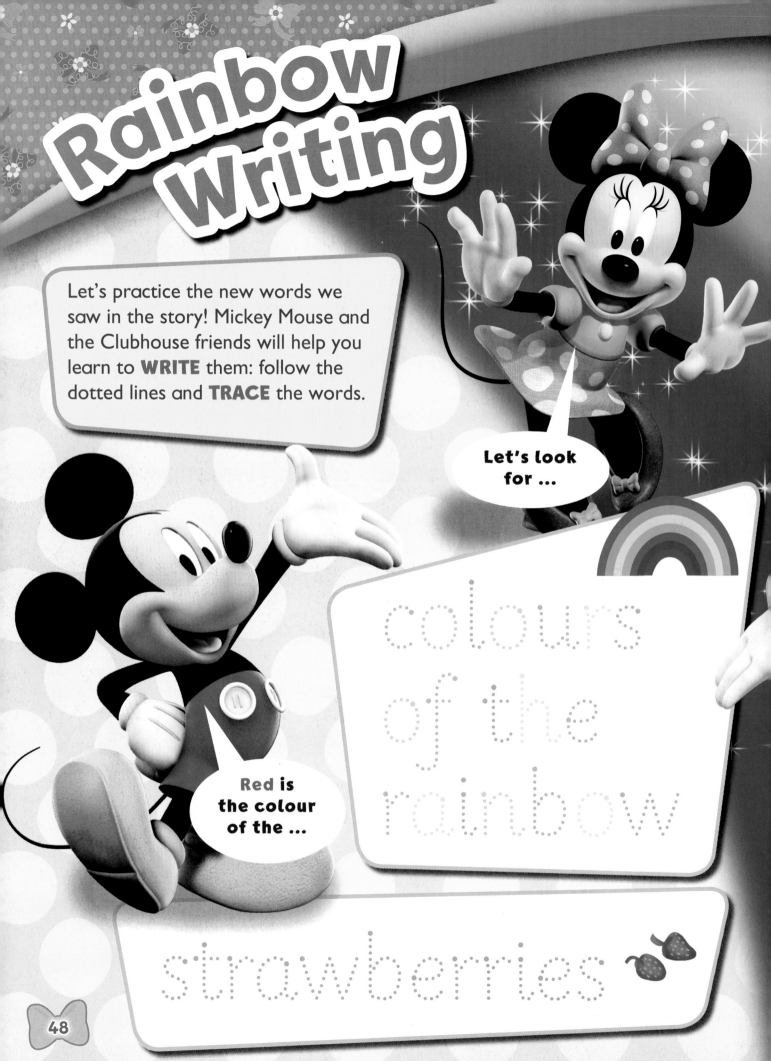

Rainbow Writing

Let's practice the new words we saw in the story! Mickey Mouse and the Clubhouse friends will help you learn to **WRITE** them: follow the dotted lines and **TRACE** the words.

Let's look for ...

Red is the colour of the ...

colours of the rainbow

strawberries

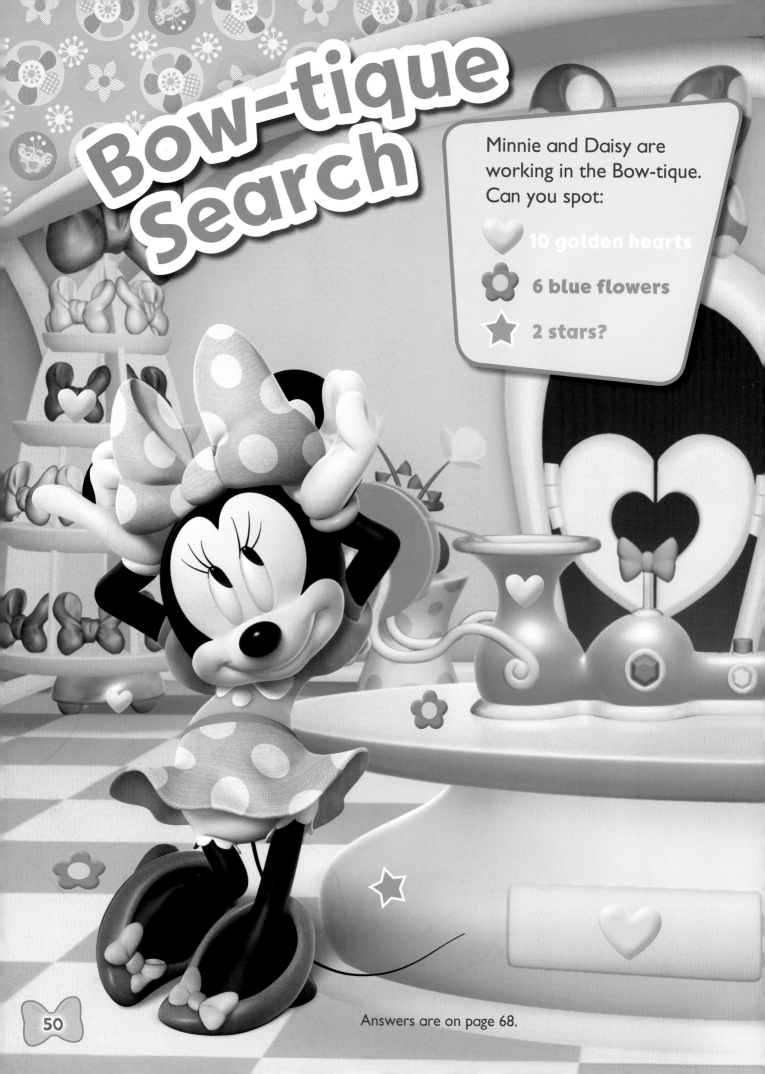

Bow-tique Search

Minnie and Daisy are working in the Bow-tique. Can you spot:

- 10 golden hearts
- 6 blue flowers
- 2 stars?

Answers are on page 68.

Point to
Cuckoo-Loca
and Figaro.

51

Secret Message

Minnie has a new shop sign. Use the code below to work out what it says.

b e o

p r s

t w y

Odd Picture Out

1

2

Help Minnie by circling the odd one out in each group of pictures.

Answers are on page 68.

Who's Minnie Meeting?

Follow the line to see who Minnie is meeting.

Minnie

START →

Daisy

Mickey

Donald

Answer on page 68.

© Disney

Bubbles of FUN

WASH

Pet Leads Puzzle

Who is walking who? Follow the leads from Daisy and Minnie to find out.

Daisy   Minnie

Bella

Figaro

Answers are on page 68.

Pet Salon Board Game

It's a busy day at the Pet Salon. Find a friend, 2 counters and a dice so you can join the fun. Take turns to throw the dice and see who gets to the **FINISH** first!

START

WASH

8

7

6

Clean puppy.
Go on 2.

5

1

2

3

Opening Time.
Go on 1.

4

Messy kitten!
Go back 2.

9 Covered in bubbles! Go back 2.

10

11 Happy puppy. Go on 2.

12

15 Smart Figaro! Go on 1.

14 Lost brush. Go back 1.

13

16

17 Beautiful Bella! Go on 2.

18

19

20

FINISH

Pet Pals Jigsaw

Can you match the missing pieces to the jigsaw picture?

Answers are on page 68.

Odd Pet Out

Draw lines to join the pet pairs. Which is the odd pet out?

Answers are on page 68.

Best in Show

Minnie has entered Bella and Figaro in a Pet Show – who do you want to win?
Colour the rosettes red for the winner and blue for the runner-up.

CUTENESS TAKES THE PRIZE

1ST PLACE FRIEND

Figaro and Cuckoo-Loca

Which picture of Figaro is the odd one out?

a

b

c

d

e

How many Cuckoo-Loca pictures can you count? Add the number in the box.

Minnie Memory Game

Play Minnie's memory game. Look at the 8 items for 20 seconds then cover them up. How many can you remember?

Goodbye!

Answers

page 10
Bow Sudoku

page 11
Counting Clothes
3 dresses, 2 bags and 4 shoes.

page 17
Minnie Mix Up
 is the odd one out.

page 19
Photo Close-Up
pictures 1, 3 and 4 can be found in the big picture.

page 20
Fly Away Maze

page 22
Can You Find?

page 26
What Comes Next?

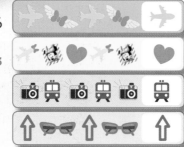

page 27
Minnie Match Up
a - 4; b - 5; c - 1;
d - 2; e - 3.

page 28
Where's Minnie Going?

Paris

page 29
Spot the Difference

page 33
Chef Minnie Matches
1 - b; 2 - c; 3 - a.

page 36
Meal Maze

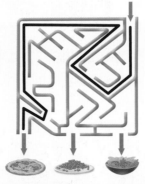

page 37
Odd One Out
the blue bow is the odd one out.

page 42
Shadow Friends
1 - d; 2 - c; 3 - a; 4 - b.

page 50
Bow-tique Search

page 52
Secret Code
the sign says pretty bows!

page 53
Odd Picture Out
group 1 = dress, group 2 = plane.

page 54
Who's Minnie Meeting?

page 57
Pet Leads Puzzle
Daisy is walking Bella and Minnie is walking Figaro.

page 60
Pet Pals Jigsaw
1 - b; 2 - c; 3 - a.

page 61
Odd Pete Out
Cuckoo-Loca is the odd pet out.

page 65
Figaro and Cuckoo-Loca
d is the odd one out. There are 5 Cuckoo-Loca pictures.